A2 Biology
UNIT 4

Edexcel

Unit 4: Respiration and Coordination

Alan Clamp

To Aristos, Dave, Jon, Jules, Paul and Pete.

Philip Allan Updates
Market Place
Deddington
Oxfordshire
OX15 0SE

tel: 01869 338652
fax: 01869 337590
e-mail: sales@philipallan.co.uk
www.philipallan.co.uk

ISBN 0 86003 471 2

This Guide has been written specifically to support students preparing for the Edexcel A2 Biology Unit 4 examination. The content has been neither approved nor endorsed by Edexcel and remains the sole responsibility of the author.

Printed by Information Press, Eynsham, Oxford

Contents

Introduction

■ ■ ■

Content Guidance

■ ■ ■

Questions and Answers

Introduction

About this guide

This unit guide is the third book in a series of four, which together cover the whole Edexcel specification for AS and A-level biology. Its aim is to help you prepare for Unit Test 4 (core) in A2 Biology which examines the content of **Unit 4: Respiration and Coordination**. (Note that this book does *not* cover the Option topics within this unit.) There are three sections to this guide:

- **Introduction** — this provides advice on how to use the unit guide, an explanation of the skills required in A2 Biology and suggestions for effective revision. It concludes with guidance on how to succeed in the unit test.
- **Content Guidance** — this summarises the specification content of Unit 4.
- **Questions and Answers** — this provides three Unit 4 mock test papers for you to try, together with sample answers to these questions and examiner's comments on how they could have been improved.

An effective way to use this book is to read through this Introduction section at the beginning of your course to familiarise yourself with the skills required in A2 biology. Try to make a habit of using the study skills and revision advice suggested in this section. It may also help to refer back to this information at regular intervals during your course.

The Content Guidance section will be useful when you are revising a topic because it highlights the main points of each subsection of the Unit 4 specification. You may want to 'tick-off' topics as you learn them to make sure that you have revised everything thoroughly.

Finally, the mock tests in the Question and Answer section will provide some very useful practice when preparing for the unit test.

The specification

In order to make a good start to Unit 4, it is important to have a close look at the specification. Your teacher should have one, or you can obtain your own copy from the awarding body (Edexcel). In addition to describing the content of the unit, the specification provides information about the unit test. It is important for you to understand the key terms used in the specification, as defined below.

- **Recall** — identify and revise biological knowledge gained from previous studies of biology.
- **Know** — be able to state facts, or describe structures and processes, from material within the unit.

- **Understand** — explain the underlying principles and apply this knowledge to new situations.
- **Appreciate** — be aware of the importance of biological information, without having a detailed knowledge of the underlying principles.
- **Discuss** —give a balanced, reasoned and objective review of a particular topic.
- **Describe** — provide an accurate account of the main points (an explanation is not necessary).
- **Explain** — give reasons, with reference to biological theories.

The specification also provides information about the skills required in A2 biology. For example, in Unit 4 approximately 60% of the marks are available for showing *knowledge and understanding* of biological information, and 40% of the marks are available for *applying* this knowledge and understanding to explain experimental data or solve problems in unfamiliar situations.

Finally, in addition to looking at the specification, it would also be useful for you to read the examiners' reports and published mark schemes from previous unit tests (these are available from Edexcel). These documents will show you the depth of knowledge that examiners are looking for in answers, as well as pointing out common mistakes and providing advice on how to achieve good grades in the tests.

Study skills and revision strategies

Students need to develop good study skills if they are to be successful. This section of the Introduction provides advice and guidance on how to study A2 biology and suggests some strategies for effective revision.

Organising your notes

Biology students usually accumulate a large quantity of notes and it is useful to keep this information in an organised manner. The presentation of notes is important; good notes should always be clear and concise. You could try organising your notes under headings and subheadings, with key points highlighted using capitals, italics or colour. Numbered lists are useful, as are tables and diagrams. It is a good idea to file your notes in specification order, using a consistent series of informative headings, as illustrated below.

UNIT 4 (Respiration and Coordination)
Regulation of the internal environment
Nervous coordination in mammals
There are several important differences between nervous and hormonal coordination...

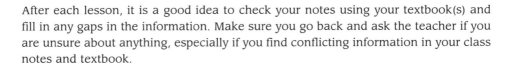

After each lesson, it is a good idea to check your notes using your textbook(s) and fill in any gaps in the information. Make sure you go back and ask the teacher if you are unsure about anything, especially if you find conflicting information in your class notes and textbook.

Organising your time

It is a good idea to make a revision timetable to ensure you use your time effectively. This should allow enough time to cover all the material, but also be realistic. For example, it is useful to leave some time at the end of the timetable, just before the unit test, to catch up on time lost, possibly through illness. You may not be able to work for very long at a single session — probably no more than 1 hour — without a short break of 10–15 minutes. It is also useful to use spare moments, such as when waiting for a bus or train, to do short snippets of revision. These 'odd minutes' can add up to many hours.

Improving your memory

There are several things you can do to improve the effectiveness of your memory for biological information. Organising the material will help, especially if you use topic headings, numbered lists and diagrams. Repeatedly reviewing your notes will also be useful, as will discussing topics with teachers and other students. Finally, using mnemonics (memory aids), such as **A**rteries carry blood **A**way from the heart, can make a big difference.

Revision strategies

To revise a topic effectively you should work carefully through your notes, using a copy of the specification to make sure you have not missed anything out. Summarise your notes to the bare essentials, using the tips given on note-making above. Finally, use the content guidance and mock examinations in this book, discussing any difficulties with your teachers or other students.

In many ways, a student should prepare for a unit test like an athlete prepares for a major event, such as the Olympic Games. The athlete will train every day for weeks or months before the event, practising the required skills in order to achieve the best performance on the day. So it is with test preparation: everything you do should contribute to your chances of success in the unit test.

The following points summarise some of the strategies that you may wish to use to make sure that your revision is as effective as possible.

- Use a revision timetable.
- Ideally, revise in a quiet room, sitting at a desk or table, with no distractions.
- Test yourself regularly to assess the effectiveness of your revision.
- Practise previous test questions to highlight gaps in your knowledge and understanding and to improve your technique.

- Active revision is much better than simply reading over material. Discuss topics, summarise notes and use the mock tests included in this book to increase the effectiveness of your revision.

The unit test

Unit Test 4 (core) consists of about five compulsory questions allocated from 4 to 12 marks each, presented in a question–answer booklet. There are 40 marks available in this part of the test and it should last for about 50 minutes (giving you around 1 ¼ minutes per mark). The shorter questions are designed mainly to test knowledge and understanding of the unit content. The longer questions also test skills in interpreting data related to the content of the unit. There is normally one free-prose question on each paper (see page 8).

Note that the option topics are also tested on this paper: either Option A (Microbiology and biotechnology), Option B (Food science) or Option C (Human health and fitness). This section of the paper is similar in style to that of the core, except that there is no free-prose question, there are only 30 marks available and it should last for about 40 minutes.

There are a number of terms commonly used in unit tests. It is important that you understand the meaning of each of these terms and that you answer the question appropriately.

- **Calculate** — carry out a calculation, showing your working and providing the appropriate units.
- **Compare** — point out similarities *and* differences.
- **Define** — give a statement outlining what is meant by a particular term.
- **Describe** — provide an accurate account of the main points. An explanation is *not* necessary.
- **Discuss** — describe and evaluate, putting forward the various opinions on a topic.
- **Distinguish between** — point out differences only.
- **Explain** — give reasons, with reference to biological facts. A description is *not* required.
- **Outline** — give a brief account.
- **Significance** — the relevance of an idea or observation.
- **State** — give a concise, factual answer (also applies to **give** or **name**).
- **Suggest** — use biological knowledge to put forward an appropriate answer in an unfamiliar situation.
- **What/Why/Where** — these indicate direct questions requiring concise answers.

Whatever the question style, you must read the question *very carefully*, underline key words or phrases, think about your response and allocate time according to the number of marks available. Further advice and guidance on answering test questions is provided in the Question and Answer section at the end of this book.

Structured questions

These are short-answer questions that may require a single-word answer, a short sentence, or a response amounting to several sentences. Answers should be clear, concise and to the point. The marks allocated and the space provided for the answer usually give an indication of the amount of detail required. Typical question styles include:

- naming parts on diagrams
- filling in gaps in a prose passage
- completing tables and tick-boxes
- plotting graphs
- performing calculations
- interpreting experimental data

Free-prose questions

These questions enable you to demonstrate the depth and breadth of your biological knowledge, as well as your ability to communicate scientific ideas in a concise and clear manner. The following points should help you to perform well when answering free-prose questions:

- make your points clearly and concisely, illustrating your answer with examples where appropriate
- try to avoid repetition and keep the answer relevant (refer back to the question)
- the points you make should cover the *full range* of the topics addressed in the question
- use diagrams only if appropriate and where they make a useful contribution to the quality of your answer
- spend the appropriate amount of time on the question (proportional to the marks available)

The day of the unit test

On the day of the test, make sure that you have:

- two or more blue/black pens, and two or more pencils
- your calculator plus spare batteries
- a watch to check the time
- a ruler and an eraser

Read each question very carefully so that your answers are appropriate. Make sure that you write legibly (you will not be given marks if the examiner cannot read what you have written) and try to spell scientific terms accurately. If you need more room for your answer, look for space at the bottom of the page, the end of the question or after the last question, or use supplementary sheets. If you use these spaces, or sheets, alert the examiner by adding 'continued below', or 'continued on page X'.

Time is often a problem. Make sure that you know how long you have got for the whole test and how many questions you have to do in this time. You could use the number of minutes per mark to work out approximately how long you have for each question (e.g. 10 minutes for an 8-mark question in Unit Test 4).

Do not write out the question, but try to make a number of valid points that correspond to the number of marks available. If you get stuck, make a note of the question number and move on. Later, if you have time, go back and try that difficult question again. Finally, it is a good idea to leave a few minutes at the end to check through your answers, correcting any mistakes or filling in any gaps.

Content
Guidance

Unit 4 of the Edexcel specification is probably the first A2 unit that you will study. It is important to realise that A2 Biology represents a step up in complexity from AS Biology (in a similar way that AS Biology was a step up from GCSE Biology). In order to understand the content of this unit, you should be familiar with all the AS material from Units 1, 2 and 3.

This book addresses the Unit 4 core topics of metabolic pathways and regulation of the internal environment.

Metabolic pathways includes the sub-topics of:

(1) Cellular respiration

(2) Aerobic respiration

(3) Anaerobic respiration

Regulation of the internal environment looks at:

(1) Mammalian kidney

(2) Regulation of blood glucose

(3) Response to changes in the external environment

(4) Chemical coordination in animals

(5) Nervous coordination in mammals

(6) The central nervous system

You may be familiar with some of the information in this unit, but it is important that you know and understand this information exactly as described in the specification. This summary of the specification content will highlight the key points and should prove very useful when learning and revising biology.

Metabolic pathways

This topic looks at processes of **metabolism**, including **respiration**, and highlights the roles of enzymes and ATP in these pathways. Before starting to learn this material, it may be useful to revise biological molecules, enzymes and the structure of a mitochondrion from Unit 1.

Metabolism

Metabolism is the sum total of all the biochemical reactions taking place within an organism. Metabolic reactions are controlled by enzymes and can be divided into two groups:

- **anabolism** — these are synthetic reactions that *require* energy, such as protein synthesis
- **catabolism** — these are breakdown reactions that *release* energy, such as respiration

The various substances involved in metabolism are called **metabolites** and the sequence of biochemical reactions is known as a **metabolic pathway**, as shown in the diagram below.

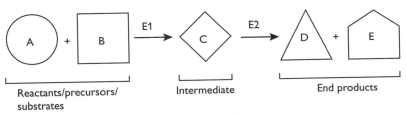

Reactants/precursors/substrates   Intermediate   End products

Note: E1 and E2 are two different enzymes. This is a very simple metabolic pathway — others may have branches or cycles (e.g. the Krebs cycle).

There are several advantages of metabolic pathways:

- metabolic reactions can proceed in a continuous manner — equilibrium is never reached because products become substrates of subsequent reactions
- the stepwise nature of most catabolic pathways enables energy to be released in small, controlled amounts
- each step is controlled by a specific enzyme and therefore each enzyme represents a point for control of the overall pathway
- the steps in the pathway may be spatially arranged so that the product of one reaction is ideally located to become the substrate in the next reaction — this makes metabolism much more efficient

One example of a metabolic pathway is respiration (described in detail below). Two important groups of enzymes controlling this process are **hydrolases** and **oxidoreductases**.

Hydrolases

Hydrolases are enzymes that catalyse the **hydrolysis** of a molecule, i.e. the molecule is broken down by the addition of water. One example of this process is the hydrolysis of glycogen to release glucose, in order that the glucose can be respired.

Oxidoreductases

Oxidoreductases are enzymes that catalyse biochemical reactions involving **oxidation** (gaining oxygen, or losing hydrogen or electrons) and **reduction** (losing oxygen, or gaining hydrogen or electrons). Oxidoreductases catalyse the transfer of hydrogen, oxygen or electrons between molecules. Several oxidoreductases are involved in the metabolic pathways of respiration, for example cytochrome oxidase is an enzyme that transfers electrons from cytochromes to oxygen (forming water) at the end of the electron transport chain.

ATP

ATP (adenosine triphosphate) is a molecule that acts as an energy carrier in all living cells. It is a nucleotide, containing ribose as its pentose sugar and adenine as its nitrogenous base. Three phosphate groups are attached to the ribose subunit. The bond attaching the end phosphate group can be hydrolysed by ATPase to yield ADP (adenosine diphosphate) and a large quantity of energy. This reaction is reversible if enough energy is supplied, and is summarised in the diagram below.

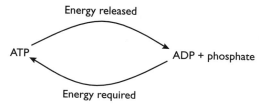

The energy required to produce ATP comes from **respiration** and **photosynthesis**.

ATP has a number of roles in living organisms, including supplying the energy required for protein synthesis, active transport and muscle contraction. It also plays a very important role in metabolism, acting as an immediate supply of energy for anabolic processes.

Cellular respiration

Respiration is the oxidation of organic molecules by cells in order to release energy. The main respiratory substrate is glucose, which is oxidised in cells to produce ATP.

Aerobic respiration involves glycolysis, the link reaction, the Krebs cycle and the electron transport chain. **Anaerobic respiration** involves only glycolysis and results in a much lower yield of ATP.

Glycolysis

Glycolysis is the first stage of respiration, in which glucose is broken down to form pyruvate. It occurs in the cytoplasm of cells and is common to both aerobic respiration and anaerobic respiration. The biochemical reactions that take place during glycolysis are summarised in the diagram below.

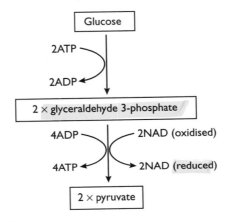

This can be summarised as:

glucose + 2NAD (oxidised) + 2ADP + $2P_i$ $\longrightarrow$ 2 × pyruvate + 2NAD (reduced) + 2ATP

Aerobic respiration

Aerobic respiration is the breakdown of glucose in the presence of oxygen to yield energy. The process of aerobic respiration is summarised in the diagram below.

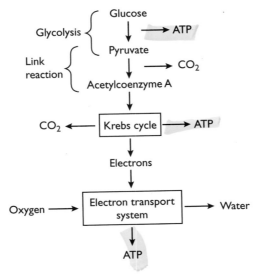

This can be summarised as:

$$glucose + oxygen + ADP + P_i \longrightarrow carbon\ dioxide + water + ATP$$

Aerobic respiration begins with glycolysis, which involves the breakdown of glucose to pyruvate, generating a small amount of ATP. If oxygen is present, pyruvate is converted to acetylcoenzyme A (releasing carbon dioxide) in the link reaction, which can be summarised by the following equation:

$$pyruvate + NAD\ (oxidised) \longrightarrow acetylcoenzyme\ A + CO_2 + NAD\ (reduced)$$

[Note that NAD (nicotinamide adenine dinucleotide) acts as a hydrogen acceptor in respiration. FAD (flavine adenine dinucleotide) is another hydrogen acceptor involved in aerobic respiration, as shown in the Krebs cycle below.] Acetylcoenzyme A then enters the Krebs cycle, where ATP, carbon dioxide and NAD (reduced) are produced. The Krebs cycle takes place in the matrix of mitochondria and the reactions can be summarised by the diagram below.

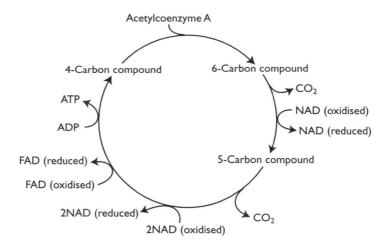

This can be summarised as:

$$\begin{array}{c} acetyl \\ (2C) \end{array} + \begin{array}{c} 2NAD \\ (oxidised) \end{array} + \begin{array}{c} 2FAD \\ (oxidised) \end{array} + ADP + P_i \longrightarrow 2CO_2 + \begin{array}{c} 2NAD \\ (reduced) \end{array} + \begin{array}{c} FAD \\ (reduced) \end{array} + ATP$$

The NAD (reduced) provides electrons that are passed along the electron transport chain, ultimately combining with oxygen to form water. The movement of electrons through the electron transport system releases a large amount of energy, which is used to produce further ATP (a process known as **oxidative phosphorylation**). The electron transport chain is found on the cristae of mitochondria, where the energy released by the transfer of electrons between carriers is used to pump protons (hydrogen ions) across the membrane. The return of the protons, through specialised protein pores in the membrane, is coupled to the synthesis of ATP. This process is summarised in the diagram below.

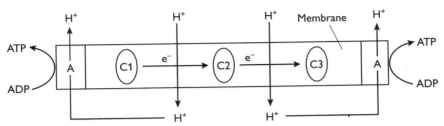

Key: H⁺ = proton; C1/C2/C3 = electron carriers; e⁻ = electron; A = ATPase

When considering the topic of aerobic respiration, it is useful to recall the structure of a mitochondrion. A mitochondrion is a rod-shaped organelle found in the cytoplasm of eukaryotic cells. The function of mitochondria is to carry out the chemical reactions involved in the Krebs cycle and the electron transport chain of aerobic respiration. The diagram below shows the general structure of a mitochondrion.

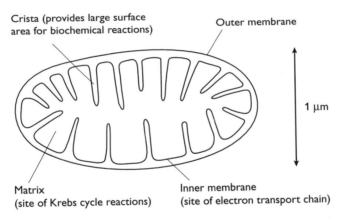

Note that cells with large energy demands, such as muscle cells or those carrying out active transport, tend to contain large numbers of mitochondria.

Anaerobic respiration

Anaerobic respiration is the breakdown of glucose in the absence of oxygen to yield energy. The process is basically the same as glycolysis and only yields 5–6% of the ATP produced by aerobic respiration (which requires oxygen). In plants and micro-organisms such as yeast, the pyruvate produced by glycolysis is converted to ethanol and carbon dioxide. In animals, the pyruvate is converted to lactic acid (lactate). In both cases, pyruvate acts as a hydrogen acceptor and NAD is oxidised. This process is vital if glycolysis (and the production of ATP) is to continue in the absence of oxygen. The process of anaerobic respiration (sometimes called fermentation) is summarised in the diagram below.

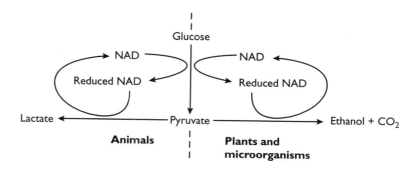

Practical work

In addition to knowing and understanding the theoretical material summarised above, you will also be expected to carry out experiments to illustrate the role of hydrogen acceptors using a redox indicator, such as methylene blue or tetrazolium chloride. You may be asked to give a detailed description of such experiments in an examination, so it is very important that you have carried them out and learned the details of the methods.

Regulation of the internal environment

This topic requires you to understand the concept of **homeostasis** and its importance in maintaining the body in a state of **dynamic equilibrium**. Homeostasis can be defined as 'the maintenance of a constant internal environment'. Cells require certain conditions to function efficiently. Intercellular fluid (and therefore blood) must contain oxygen and nutrients, and have the optimum pH, temperature and water potential. Homeostasis represents the set of physiological mechanisms involved in regulating this internal environment. Most homeostatic mechanisms are coordinated by hormones and involve **negative feedback**, as shown in the diagram below.

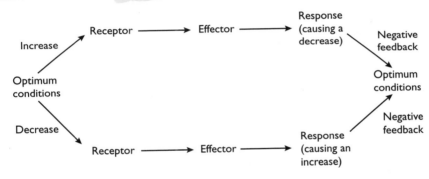

Note that if a physiological factor deviates from its optimum, the deviation is sensed and negative feedback mechanisms are used to return the factor to its optimum. **Positive feedback** is a condition in which the deviation of a physiological factor from its optimum causes further deviation to occur. For example, if the body temperature falls *significantly* below the optimum, the metabolic rate also falls (because enzyme activity is reduced at lower temperatures). This means that less heat is produced and the body temperature will fall further. Ultimately, this process may lead to hypothermia and even death.

Examples of homeostasis include **thermoregulation** (the control of body temperature in animals), the control of respiratory gases in the blood and the regulation of blood glucose (see page 22). It is important to understand that homeostasis allows organisms to be independent of the external environment. Therefore, animals with efficient homeostatic mechanisms (such as mammals) can survive in a wide range of habitats.

Mammalian kidney

The kidneys are a pair of organs found in mammals. They play an important role in **excretion** and **osmoregulation**. Each kidney is composed of millions of nephrons, which are the structural and functional units of the organs. The nephrons are responsible for ultrafiltration, the selective reabsorption of useful products and the excretion of nitrogenous waste in the form of urine. They also regulate the removal of water from the body and are therefore important in osmoregulation.

Excretion is the removal of the waste products of cellular metabolism. Note that **defecation** (the removal of faeces) is *not* the same as excretion, because the waste materials are not the products of cellular metabolism. Also, try not to confuse excretion with *secretion*, which is the transport of *useful* substances to their place of action.

The general structure of a nephron is shown below.

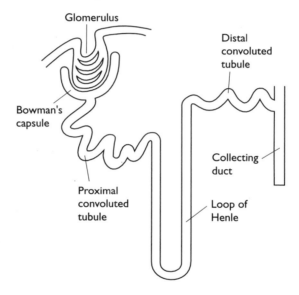

Fluid enters the Bowman's capsule by ultrafiltration (filtration that occurs on a molecular scale) from the blood. This glomerular filtrate consists of blood plasma minus the large plasma proteins. Useful substances, such as glucose, amino acids and some salts and water, are reabsorbed back into the blood as the filtrate passes through the nephron. The end product is a relatively concentrated solution of urea (the main nitrogenous waste product of mammals), salts and water, known as urine, which passes out of the body via the bladder. (Remember that glomerular filtrate contains many useful substances filtered out of the blood, such as glucose. These substances have to be reabsorbed from the nephron back into the blood. Glomerular filtrate is therefore *not* the same as urine.)

The loop of Henle is the hairpin-shaped section of a kidney nephron, situated between the proximal convoluted tubule and the distal convoluted tubule. It consists of a thin descending limb, which is permeable to water, and a thick ascending limb, which is impermeable to water. Movement of ions across the walls of the loop of Henle enables it to act as a countercurrent multiplier, building up the concentration of sodium in the medulla of the kidney. This process results in the production of concentrated urine in the collecting duct, as shown in the diagram below.

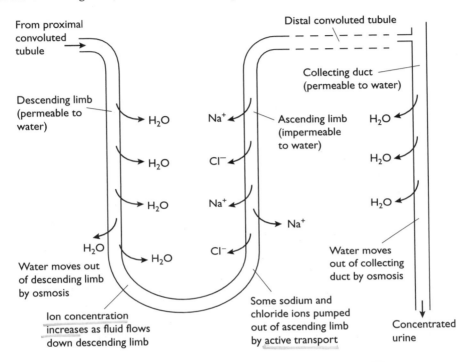

From proximal convoluted tubule

Distal convoluted tubule

Descending limb (permeable to water)

Collecting duct (permeable to water)

H_2O Na^+ Ascending limb (impermeable to water) H_2O

H_2O Cl^- H_2O

H_2O Na^+ H_2O

Na^+

H_2O Cl^- Water moves out of collecting duct by osmosis

H_2O

Water moves out of descending limb by osmosis

Ion concentration increases as fluid flows down descending limb

Some sodium and chloride ions pumped out of ascending limb by active transport

Concentrated urine

Note that a longer loop of Henle will result in the production of more concentrated urine. Therefore animals that live in arid regions, such as the kangaroo rat, have relatively long loops of Henle to conserve water; those living in water-rich regions, such as the beaver, have shorter loops of Henle.

Osmoregulation

Osmoregulation is the ability of an organism to regulate the water potential of its body fluids. It is an example of homeostasis that involves monitoring the water potential inside the body and responding to changes by excreting or absorbing and retaining water (and salts). The kidneys play a vital role in osmoregulation in mammals. **Antidiuretic hormone (ADH)** is a hormone that makes the distal convoluted tubules and collecting ducts of a kidney nephron more permeable to water. ADH is released by the pituitary gland in response to a fall in the water potential of the blood. Its effect on the kidney means that more water is reabsorbed into the blood (increasing its water potential) and less is lost in the urine. In other words, ADH prevents the production of large quantities of watery urine (diuresis), hence its name: antidiuretic hormone. The flow chart below summarises the way in which ADH helps to control water balance in the body.

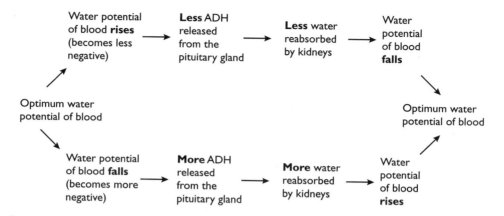

Aldosterone is another hormone involved in osmoregulation. It regulates the concentration of sodium ions in the blood. Aldosterone is secreted by the adrenal gland in response to a fall in the sodium ion concentration of the blood. It increases the active transport of sodium ions from the kidney tubules into the blood.

Regulation of blood glucose

Glucose is a hexose (six-carbon) monosaccharide with the molecular formula $C_6H_{12}O_6$. It is the main substrate for respiration and therefore a vital nutrient for all living cells. It is important to regulate the concentration of glucose in the blood in order to maintain the supply to respiring cells and to avoid **hyperglycaemia** (an abnormally high level of glucose in the blood, resulting in dehydration and weight loss) or **hypoglycaemia** (an abnormally low level of glucose in the blood, resulting in tiredness, sweating and possibly coma). These conditions are relatively common in people suffering from **diabetes**, which is a disease in which the concentration of glucose in the blood cannot be properly regulated. There are two types of diabetes:

- **insulin-dependent diabetes**, in which the pancreas fails to produce enough insulin to control the concentration of glucose in the blood. Excess glucose appears in the urine, leading to weight loss and dehydration. The disease can be controlled by regulating the diet and injecting insulin.
- **non-insulin-dependent diabetes**, in which the pancreas produces enough insulin, but the cells of the body fail to take up glucose in response to the hormone. The disease can only be controlled by carefully regulating the diet.

The regulation of blood glucose is therefore a vital homeostatic process. It is controlled by two hormones secreted by islets of Langerhans in the pancreas: the **α-cells** secrete **glucagon**; the **β-cells** secrete **insulin**. Glucagon is secreted in response to a *decreased* concentration of glucose in the blood and brings about an increase in the blood glucose level, as shown in the diagram below.

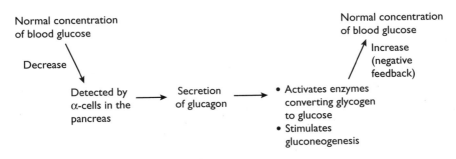

Gluconeogenesis is the synthesis of glucose from non-carbohydrate sources, such as lipid and protein. It occurs when the blood glucose level is low and glycogen stores in the liver have been depleted. The synthesis of glucose is essentially a reversal of glycolysis. It can use many sources, such as amino acids and glycerol. (Remember not to confuse glucagon with *glycogen*, which is a storage carbohydrate found in animals. The words look very similar, so it is vital that you use the correct spelling.)

Insulin is **antagonistic** to glucagon, which means that the two hormones have opposite effects on the blood glucose concentration. Insulin is secreted in response to an *increased* concentration of glucose in the blood and brings about a decrease in the blood glucose level, as shown in the diagram below.

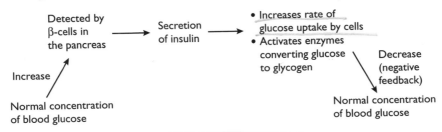

Adrenaline, another hormone, stimulates **glycogenolysis** (the conversion of glycogen to glucose) and therefore it increases the concentration of blood glucose.

Responses to changes in the external environment

Animals and plants have sensory receptors designed to detect external stimuli (e.g. light) and initiate a response. **Photoreceptors**, for example, are cells that are sensitive to light. Most photoreceptors contain a **pigment** that is chemically changed by light, thus stimulating an action potential or hormonal response.

Photoreceptors in animals are often grouped together to form specialised light-sensitive organs, such as eyes. The **retina** is a layer of light-sensitive cells, called rod cells and cone cells, found at the back of the eye. The differences between these two cell types are summarised in the table below.

Feature	Rods	Cones
Location	Throughout the retina (except in the fovea)	Concentrated in the fovea
Sensitivity to light	Higher	Lower
Colour vision	No	Yes
Visual acuity	Low	High

(retinal)

Rod cells contain the pigment **rhodopsin**, which consists of a protein, opsin, linked to retinine (a derivative of vitamin A). The presence of light causes rhodopsin to split into its two components, initiating the transmission of a nerve impulse along the optic nerve to the brain. Before it can be stimulated again, rhodopsin must be resynthesised from opsin and retinine. This is an anabolic reaction and requires ATP.

Cone cells contain a similar light-sensitive pigment, known as **iodopsin**. This pigment has three different forms which are maximally sensitive to either red, blue or green light. The relative activity of these red, blue and green cone cells determines the colour that is observed.

Phytochrome is a pigment found in plants which is important in regulating growth. It exists in two forms. P_R has a maximum light absorption peak in red light of wavelength 660 nm, whereas P_{FR} absorbs maximally in far red light at 730 nm. The two forms are interconvertible, as shown in the diagram below.

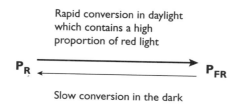

Rapid conversion in daylight which contains a high proportion of red light

P_R ⟶ P_{FR}

Slow conversion in the dark

P_{FR} is thought to be metabolically active and influences a number of light-related processes, including germination and flowering.

Chemical coordination in animals

Hormones are chemical messengers that are transported in the blood. They are secreted into the blood by endocrine glands and then transported to target cells, where they bind to specific receptors on the cell surface membrane. The hormones then influence the physiology of the cells in some way, by changing membrane permeability, altering the activity of enzymes, or activating or inhibiting genes.

Examples of hormones are described earlier in this Content Guidance section. These include insulin, glucagon and antidiuretic hormone (ADH). Another important group of hormones is those involved in sexual reproduction. They are summarised below.

- **Follicle-stimulating hormone (FSH)** — a mammalian hormone that stimulates the production of gametes. FSH is secreted by the anterior lobe of the pituitary gland and stimulates the production of ova (eggs) in females and sperm in males.
- **Luteinising hormone (LH)** — a hormone that stimulates ovulation in females and the production of testosterone in males. LH is released by the anterior lobe of the pituitary gland. In addition to the functions described above, it also stimulates the development of the corpus luteum and the subsequent secretion of progesterone in females.
- **Oestrogen** — a sex hormone produced by the ovaries in females. Oestrogen plays an important role in the regulation of the menstrual cycle, the maintenance of pregnancy and the development of female secondary sexual characteristics, such as breasts.
- **Progesterone** — a sex hormone produced by the ovaries in females. Progesterone is secreted by the corpus luteum and plays an important role in the regulation of the menstrual cycle. During the first few weeks of pregnancy, the corpus luteum continues to secrete progesterone, but in the later stages this role is taken over by the placenta. Progesterone maintains the lining of the uterus for implantation and inhibits contraction of the uterine muscles.
- **Testosterone** — a sex hormone produced by the testis in males. Testosterone controls the growth and development of the male sex organs and also influences protein synthesis and bone growth. In addition, it regulates sexual behaviour and the development of the male secondary sexual characteristics, such as a deep voice and facial hair.

Nervous coordination in mammals

There are several key differences between nervous and hormonal coordination, as summarised in the table below.

Feature	Nervous coordination	Hormonal coordination
Speed	Fast	Slow
Duration of response	Short-lived	Longer-lasting
Nature of information	Electrical	Chemical
Specificity	Specific (localised effects)	Often widespread

A **neurone** is a cell specialised for the conduction of nerve impulses. Neurones are well adapted for conducting impulses, having an elongated shape and specialised structures to form connections with receptors, effectors and other neurones via synapses. Many neurones are coated with **myelin** (a mixture of phospholipid and cholesterol) which insulates the neurone and helps to speed up the conduction of impulses. There are three basic types of neurone:

- **sensory neurones** transmit impulses from a receptor to the central nervous system
- **motor neurones** transmit impulses from the central nervous system to an effector
- **intermediate neurones** connect sensory and motor neurones within the central nervous system

Receptors are cells that are specialised to detect a particular stimulus. If the stimulus exceeds a minimum threshold value, the receptor is depolarised and an **action potential** is set up in a sensory neurone. Receptors are often grouped together to form sense organs, such as eyes or ears. Examples of receptors include baroreceptors (blood pressure), chemoreceptors (blood pH) and rods and cones (light) in the retina of the eye.

Effectors are cells or organs that respond to a stimulus. In animals, muscles and glands are both effectors that respond to stimulation by a nerve impulse or a hormone. A typical sequence of events involving a response to a stimulus is shown below.

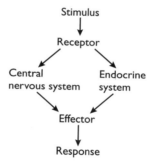

An **impulse** is a signal that travels along a neurone. Information is transmitted through the nervous system by impulses. The generation of an impulse, and its transmission along a neurone, is described in the diagram below.

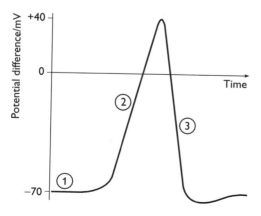

① Resting potential: a high concentration of sodium ions (Na^+) outside the cell. The inside is negative relative to the outside

② Depolarisation: stimulation of the nerve cell causes sodium ions to enter the cell, making it positive relative to the outside

③ Repolarisation: potassium ions (K^+) leave the cell, restoring the negative potential difference. A sodium–potassium pump then restores the true resting potential by actively transporting potassium into the cell and sodium out

The rapid change in electrical charge across the membrane of a nerve cell, causing the transmission of an impulse, is known as an **action potential**. In other words, stimulation of a nerve cell causes the electrical charge across the membrane to change from the resting potential of −70 mV to +40 mV. The change in electrical charge, which lasts for only a few milliseconds before the resting potential is restored, is the action potential.

All-or-nothing is a term used to describe the fact that action potentials in nerve cells are always identical in size. A stimulus will either trigger an action potential of a fixed size, or it will fail to trigger an impulse at all. A bigger stimulus will *not* trigger a bigger action potential. Therefore, the only way that information about the size of a stimulus can be transmitted is by changing the frequency of the impulses. A large stimulus will trigger high-frequency impulses and a small stimulus will trigger low-frequency impulses.

The **refractory period** is the time interval during which a nerve cell is incapable of responding to a stimulus. After a nerve cell has responded to a stimulus, certain ionic movement must occur and the resting potential has to be restored. During these processes, the nerve cell is incapable of responding to a second stimulus. A typical refractory period lasts for approximately 3 ms and this limits the number of impulses that can be transmitted along a nerve cell in a given period of time.

(Note that students often have difficulty when trying to describe the nature of a nerve impulse in examinations. Make sure that you learn this information thoroughly. Remember that nerves carry impulses and *not* messages.)

The junction between two nerve cells is known as a **synapse**. The swollen tip of the axon of the pre-synaptic neurone is called a synaptic knob. It contains vesicles of **neurotransmitter** (e.g. noradrenaline or acetylcholine) which are used to transmit the impulse to the post-synaptic neurone. The mechanism by which a synapse transmits an impulse from one nerve cell to the next is summarised in the flow chart below.

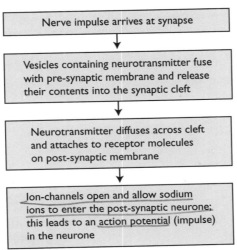

Nerve impulse arrives at synapse

↓

Vesicles containing neurotransmitter fuse with pre-synaptic membrane and release their contents into the synaptic cleft

↓

Neurotransmitter diffuses across cleft and attaches to receptor molecules on post-synaptic membrane

↓

Ion-channels open and allow sodium ions to enter the post-synaptic neurone: this leads to an action potential (impulse) in the neurone

Nicotine (a drug found in tobacco) has a similar effect to acetylcholine at some synapses, having an excitatory effect on the post-synaptic cell. In large concentrations, nicotine can block synaptic transmission after initial stimulation.

Summation is the process that occurs in synapses due to the additive effect of a number of stimuli. The arrival of an impulse at a synapse may not be sufficient to trigger an action potential in the post-synaptic cell (usually because there is not enough neurotransmitter released). However, two or more impulses arriving at the synapse in a short period of time may generate an action potential. This is known as temporal summation as the effects of the impulses add up over time. Similarly, an action potential may be triggered if several synapses act at the same time on the post-synaptic cell. This is known as spatial summation. The process of summation is important in controlling the movement of nerve impulses through the body.

The point at which a motor neurone connects with a muscle is known as a **neuro-muscular junction**. Impulses are transmitted from the motor neurone to the muscle by acetylcholine (a neurotransmitter). Acetylcholine is released from the end of the neurone and depolarises the surface membrane of a muscle fibre. This triggers an action potential in the muscle, leading to contraction. Therefore, the action of a neuromuscular junction is very similar to that of a synapse.

Practical work

This section of the specification for Unit 4 requires you to have undertaken practical work including reaction–time experiments and microscopic examination of the histology of the spinal cord. Questions relating to these practical activities may appear on the written examination papers.

The central nervous system

The central nervous system (CNS) consists of the **brain** and **spinal cord**, and is responsible for coordinating the activities of the nervous system. The brain is the organ that is responsible for controlling bodily functions by coordinating the activities of the nervous system. The structure and functions of the major parts of the human brain are shown in the diagram below.

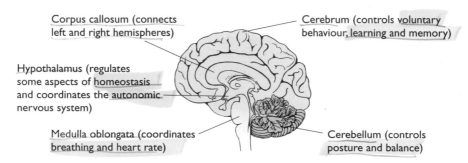

Corpus callosum (connects left and right hemispheres)

Cerebrum (controls voluntary behaviour, learning and memory)

Hypothalamus (regulates some aspects of homeostasis and coordinates the autonomic nervous system)

Medulla oblongata (coordinates breathing and heart rate)

Cerebellum (controls posture and balance)

The spinal cord is the part of the central nervous system that is enclosed by the backbone. It consists of a central cavity containing cerebrospinal fluid, surrounded by a core of grey matter (non-myelinated neurones) and an outer layer of white matter (myelinated neurones). The white matter contains numerous longitudinal neurones which conduct impulses to and from the brain. The spinal cord also plays an impor-tant part in coordinating many **reflexes**. Reflexes are rapid automatic responses to particular stimuli, which are mediated by a simple nervous circuit called a reflex arc, as shown in the diagram below.

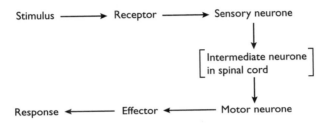

For example, if a hand is accidentally placed on a hot object, it is quickly pulled away. Reflexes are also important in responding to internal changes, such as the need for more oxygen in the blood, leading to an increase in the breathing rate.

Questions
&
Answers

In this section of the guide there are three mock papers written in the same format as the real unit test papers. All questions are based on the topic areas outlined in the Content Guidance section. When you have completed a paper, ideally under timed conditions (allowing 50 minutes per paper — see page 7), compare your answers with those of Candidate A and Candidate B. Try to avoid looking at the sample answers and examiner's comments before completing the tests. Make sure that you correct any mistakes and that you study the examiner's comments very carefully. You will get a much better grade if you can avoid the common errors made by candidates in their unit tests.

Examiner's comments

Candidate responses include examiner's comments after each section of the answer. These examiner's comments are preceded by the icon 🖉 and indicate where credit is due. In the weaker answers, they also point out areas for improvement, specific problems and common errors, such as poor time management, lack of clarity, weak or non-existent development, irrelevance, misinterpretation of the question and mistaken meanings of terms.

Respiration and coordination (I)

(1) The table below refers to the location and function of three parts of the brain. Complete the table by writing the name of the part of the brain, its location or one function in the boxes provided.

Part of brain	Location	One function
Hypothalamus	Forebrain	
		Coordinates heart rate
	Hindbrain	

5 marks

(2) (a) Explain what is meant by the following terms:
    (i) metabolic pathway   (2 marks)
    (ii) oxidoreductase   (2 marks)
  (b) Why is ATP important in metabolism?   (1 mark)

Total: 5 marks

(3) (a) State two differences between nervous and hormonal coordination.   (2 marks)
  (b) The graph below shows the changes in permeability of the cell surface membrane of an axon to sodium and potassium ions during an action potential.

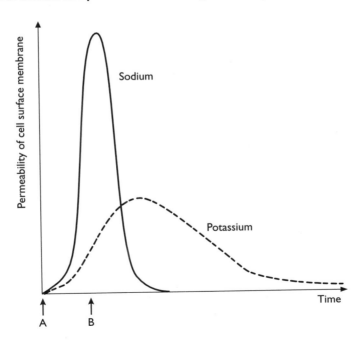

mock paper

Explain how the events that take place between times **A** and **B** on the graph can lead to a change in the potential difference across the membrane. (2 marks)

(c) Suggest why, during a period of intense nervous activity, the metabolic rate of a nerve cell increases. (2 marks)

(d) What would be the effect on an action potential of lowering the external concentration of sodium ions? Explain your answer. (2 marks)

Total: 8 marks

(4) A person fasted overnight and then consumed 80 g of glucose. The graph below shows the resulting changes in the concentrations of glucose and insulin in the blood of this person.

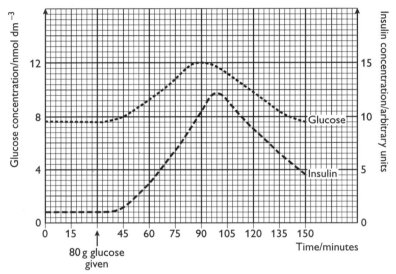

(a) (i) Describe the changes in the concentration of glucose in the blood between 30 minutes and 150 minutes. (2 marks)

(ii) Calculate the percentage increase in the concentration of insulin in the blood between 60 minutes and 90 minutes. Show your working. (3 marks)

(iii) Explain the relationship between the concentrations of glucose and insulin in the blood between 30 minutes and 150 minutes. (3 marks)

(iv) Use the information from the graph to explain what is meant by the term *negative feedback*. (2 marks)

(b) Explain why the concentration of glucagon in the blood rises during exercise, while that of insulin falls. (2 marks)

Total: 12 marks

(5) Give an account of the process of anaerobic respiration. **10 marks**

Respiration and coordination (II)

(1) Read the following passage about hormones and then write on the dotted lines the most appropriate word or words to complete the passage.

Hormones are usually either proteins, polypeptides or .... Most hormones are produced by .... glands, which release them directly into the blood. Hormones bind to .... on the cell surface membrane of .... cells, where they bring about a response. The release of hormones is controlled by a mechanism known as ....

5 marks

(2) The diagram below shows a motor neurone.

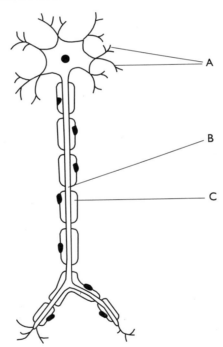

(a) Identify the structures labelled A, B and C in the diagram.　　(3 marks)
(b) Give *two* functions of the structure labelled C in the diagram.　　(2 marks)

Total: 5 marks

(3) (a) Explain what is meant by the term *homeostasis*.　　(2 marks)
　　　(b) The graph below shows the changes in blood glucose concentration in a healthy person and in a diabetic over a 3 hour period following a meal.

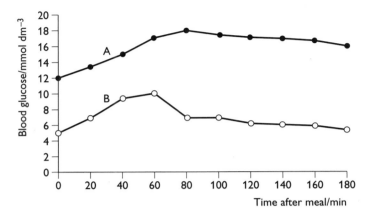

(i) **Compare curve A and curve B over the 3 hour period.** (3 marks)

(ii) **Which curve represents the blood glucose concentration of the diabetic person? Explain your answer.** (3 marks)

Total: 8 marks

(4) The diagram below summarises the process of anaerobic respiration.

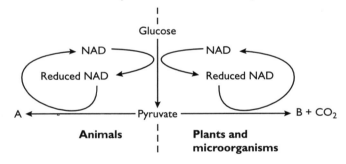

(a) **Identify compounds A and B.** (2 marks)

(b) **An experiment was carried out to investigate the effect of temperature on anaerobic respiration in yeast cells. Respiring yeast cells were incubated at different temperatures in a sucrose solution to which methylene blue, a redox indicator, had been added. After 20 minutes, the light absorbance of the suspension was measured using a colorimeter and the rate of respiration was calculated. The results of the investigation are shown in the table below.**

Temperature/°C	Rate of respiration/ arbitrary units
10	5.6
20	10.2
30	18.4
40	32.8

(i) Explain the role of redox indicators, such as methylene blue, in experiments of this kind. (3 marks)

(ii) Suggest *one* precaution that should be taken when carrying out this experiment to ensure that the results are reliable. (2 marks)

(iii) Calculate the Q_{10} for the yeast respiration between 20°C and 30°C. Show your working. (2 marks)

(iv) Explain why temperature should affect the rate of respiration of yeast cells in this way. (3 marks)

Total: 12 marks

(5) Give an account of ultrafiltration and selective reabsorption in the mammalian kidney. **10 marks**

Respiration and coordination (III)

(1) The statements in the table below refer to rod cells and cone cells in the retina. If the statement is correct, place a tick (✔) in the appropriate box and if the statement is incorrect, place a cross (✘) in the appropriate box.

Statement	Rod cells	Cone cells
Contain the pigment rhodopsin		
Used for colour vision		
Sensitive to light		
Found mainly in the fovea		
Work most efficiently at low light intensities		

5 marks

(2) The flow chart below summarises the process of aerobic respiration.

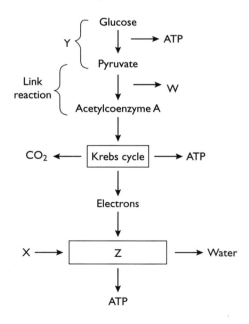

(a) Identify molecules **W** and **X** in the flow chart.   (2 marks)

(b) Identify processes **Y** and **Z** in the flow chart.   (2 marks)

(c) Where in a cell does the Krebs cycle take place? (1 mark)

Total: 5 marks

(3) The graph below shows the change in membrane potential during the passage of a nerve impulse.

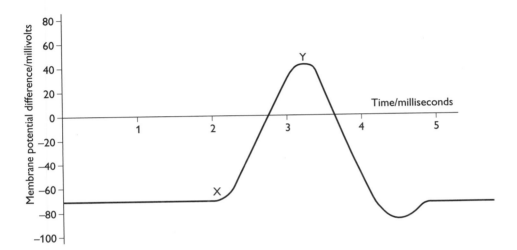

(a) (i) What is the resting potential of this neurone? (1 mark)

(ii) Explain how ion movements bring about the change in membrane potential between points **X** and **Y** on the graph. (2 marks)

(b) The mechanism by which a synapse transmits an impulse from one nerve cell to the next is summarised in the flow chart below.

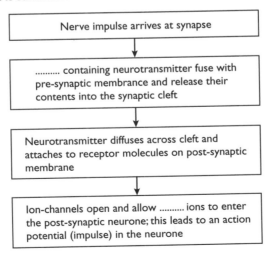

(i) Complete the flow chart by writing the appropriate word or words on the dotted lines. (2 marks)

(ii) **Curare is a poisonous chemical that competes with acetylcholine molecules for receptors at neuromuscular junctions. Suggest how an injection of curare into the bloodstream of a person may cause death by respiratory failure.** (3 marks)

Total: 8 marks

(4) The flow chart below summarises the homeostatic regulation of water potential of human blood.

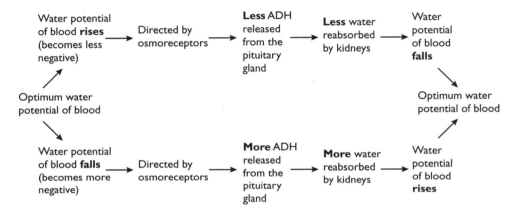

(a) (i) **Where in the body are the osmoreceptors located?** (1 mark)

(ii) **Name the gland that produces antidiuretic hormone (ADH).** (1 mark)

(b) **Ethanol (alcohol) is a chemical that inhibits the release of ADH. Suggest what will happen to the water potential of the blood of a person who has consumed ethanol.** (3 marks)

(c) **The average length of a loop of Henle in an organism is related to the concentration of urine produced according to the formula given below:**

$$y = 0.72x + 4$$

where y = the concentration of urine (arbitrary units); and x = the average length of a loop of Henle (mm). Use this formula to calculate the average length of a loop of Henle in an organism that typically produces urine of concentration 17.5 units. Show your working. (3 marks)

(d) **Animals living in arid (dry) environments tend to have relatively long loops of Henle in their kidneys and high concentrations of ADH in their blood. Suggest an explanation for these observations.** (4 marks)

Total: 12 marks

(5) Give an account of the regulation of blood glucose in a mammal. **10 marks**

Answers to mock paper 1: Candidate A

(1)

Part of brain	Location	One function
Hypothalamus	Forebrain	Breathing ✗
Medulla ✓	Midbrain ✗	Coordinates heart rate
Cerebellum ✓	Hindbrain	Intelligence ✗

*This answer earns 2 out of 5 marks. The hypothalamus does *not* control breathing (that is another function of the medulla). Correct answers for the function of the hypothalamus could be: **it coordinates the activities of the autonomic nervous system (ANS)**; **it controls hormone secretion by the pituitary gland**; or **it regulates thirst and hunger**. In the second line, the medulla is *not* located in the midbrain; it is found in the **hindbrain**. The cerebellum has been correctly identified in the third line, but its function is *not* intelligence. The cerebellum **controls balance and posture** or **coordinates skeletal muscles**.*

(2) (a) (i) A combination of anabolic and catabolic reactions ✓.

*This is correct, but only worth 1 mark. A metabolic pathway is **a sequence of biochemical reactions controlled by enzymes**. These reactions can be divided into anabolism (the synthesis of complex molecules from simple molecules, e.g. photosynthesis) and catabolism (the breakdown of complex molecules into simple molecules, e.g. respiration).*

(ii) An enzyme used in metabolism ✓.

Again, this is correct, but only worth 1 mark. The suffix 'ase' indicates that oxido-reductase is an enzyme (for 1 mark), but all enzymes are used in metabolism and therefore the second part of the answer is too vague. An oxidoreductase is an enzyme that catalyses biochemical reactions involving oxidation and reduction. Oxidoreductases catalyse the transfer of hydrogen, oxygen or electrons between molecules, e.g. cytochrome oxidase is an enzyme that transfers electrons from cytochromes to oxygen (forming water) at the end of the electron transport chain in aerobic respiration.

(b) ATP supplies the energy needed for metabolic reactions ✓.

A correct answer, for 1 mark. Overall, Candidate A scores 3 out of 5 marks for this question.

(3) (a) Nervous coordination is generally more rapid than hormonal coordination ✓. The effects of a nervous impulse are usually more specific (localised) than those of a hormone, although hormonal effects can be very specific due to the siting of receptors on the surface membrane of target cells ✓.

📝 An excellent answer, worth full marks.

(b) There is a high concentration of sodium ions inside the cell; when it is stimulated these ions leave, causing a change in potential difference across the membrane ✗.

📝 Candidate A receives no marks for this answer. A high concentration of sodium ions is found *outside* the cell. Stimulation of the axon leads to an increase in the permeability of the cell surface membrane, causing **an influx of sodium ions which change the potential difference across the membrane from negative** (approximately −70 mV) **to positive** (approximately +40 mV).

(c) The nerve cell is working hard and so its metabolic rate increases ✗.

📝 This answer is very vague and not worth any marks. Candidate A should have been more specific about the energy requirements of the nerve cell, such as mentioning that **ATP is needed for the active transport of sodium ions out of the nerve cell** (to restore the resting potential) and that **ATP is also needed for the release of neurotransmitter during the passage of an impulse across a synapse.** Therefore, **the metabolic rate increases in order to provide the ATP needed by these processes**.

(d) It would make the action potential bigger, because it would increase the concentration gradient between the sodium ions inside and outside the axon ✗.

📝 Candidate A has made two mistakes in this answer. First, the action potential *cannot* change size because of the **all-or-nothing law** (a stimulus will either trigger an action potential of a fixed size, or it will fail to trigger an impulse at all). Second, lowering the external concentration of sodium ions would *reduce* the concentration gradient between the inside and the outside of the axon. This means that **fewer sodium ions would enter the axon following stimulation, making an action potential less likely**. Overall, Candidate A scores 2 out of 8 marks for this question.

(4) (a) (i) The glucose concentration rises steadily up to 90 minutes ✓ and then falls back to its original level at 150 minutes ✓.

📝 A good answer, although Candidate A could have given the *figures* for glucose concentration.

(ii) It rises from 3 to 8.4 units ✓.

📝 Candidate A has correctly identified the two insulin concentrations from the graph. However, this is only worth 1 mark as Candidate A has not answered the question set. **The percentage increase = [(8.4 − 3)/3] × 100 = 180%.**

(iii) They both rise between 30 minutes and 90 minutes (100 minutes for insulin) and then fall back by 150 minutes ✗.

🖉 This answer is not worth any marks. The main problem is that Candidate A has *described* the changes in glucose and insulin concentrations (not a particularly detailed description in any case) rather than *explaining* the relationship. It is important to *read the question* and produce your answer accordingly. A better answer would be as follows. **As the glucose concentration starts to rise, this stimulates the release of insulin from the β-cells in the islets of Langerhans in the pancreas. As the glucose concentration continues to rise (due to absorption by the blood), more and more insulin is released. Insulin eventually causes the concentration of glucose to fall by stimulating its uptake by liver and muscle cells. This then means that the insulin secretion decreases.**

(iv) Negative feedback is a mechanism used in homeostasis for maintaining optimum conditions in the body ✓.

🖉 Although this answer is correct, it is only worth 1 mark because it has not referred to the information in the graph (as required by the question). In order to get the second mark, Candidate A needed to mention that **an increase in glucose concentration triggers the release of insulin which, in turn, causes a decrease in the concentration of glucose.**

(b) Exercise means that the skeletal muscles will be rapidly respiring and therefore using a lot of glucose ✓. Therefore, homeostatic mechanisms will be required to stimulate the entry of glucose in the blood. Since glucagon causes a rise in blood glucose concentration, this hormone will be secreted by the pancreas ✓ **(MAX)**. Insulin (which causes the concentration of blood glucose to fall) will not be secreted.

🖉 An excellent answer for 2 out of 2 marks. The examiner has written **MAX** after 2 marks have been awarded, even though the answer continues. The last point would be worth a mark, but the candidate has already achieved the maximum. This tends to happen more in free prose answers. Overall, Candidate A scores 6 out of 12 marks for this question.

(5) Anaerobic respiration is the breakdown of glucose in the absence of oxygen to yield energy ✓. It is essentially the same as glycolysis, which means that glucose is converted to pyruvate ✓ in mitochondria, yielding 4 molecules of ATP. This is much less than that produced by aerobic respiration ✓. In plants and micro-organisms such as yeast, the pyruvate is then converted to alcohol ✓. In animals, the pyruvate is converted to lactic acid ✓. Lactic acid is bad for muscles, so it is sent to the liver to be broken down ✓.

🖉 This answer is worth 6 out of 10 marks. More detail could have been provided about glycolysis, which takes place in the cytoplasm and *not* in mitochondria. Furthermore, glycolysis yields 2 molecules of ATP, not 4 molecules as stated in the answer. To be slightly more accurate, anaerobic respiration only yields 5–6% of the ATP produced by aerobic respiration (which requires oxygen). The statement that pyruvate is converted to alcohol in plants and microorganisms is correct, but it would be better to use the term ethanol and to remember that carbon dioxide is also a product of this reaction. Finally, it would have been useful to point out the importance of pyruvate acting as a hydrogen acceptor in anaerobic respiration, in order to regenerate NAD so that glycolysis can continue (so ATP is produced).

 Overall, Candidate A scores 19 out of 40 marks for this paper, which would be a grade D/E.

Answers to mock paper 1: Candidate B

(1)

Part of brain	Location	One function
Hypothalamus	Forebrain	Regulates hunger ✓
Medulla ✓	Hindbrain ✓	Coordinates heart rate
Cerebral hemispheres ✗	Hindbrain	Controls balance ✓

ℓ This answer earns 4 out of 5 marks. Candidate B has confused the cerebral hemispheres (or cerebrum), which control voluntary behaviour, learning and memory, with the correct answer of **cerebellum**. These words look similar, so make sure that you do not get them mixed up.

(2) (a) (i) A sequence of biochemical reactions, made up of a combination of anabolism and catabolism ✓.

ℓ This is correct, but worth only 1 mark. All metabolic pathways are **controlled by enzymes** and it is important to make this point if you want to score full marks.

(ii) An enzyme that catalyses biochemical reactions ✓ involving oxidation and reduction ✓.

ℓ A good, concise definition, worth 2 marks. Remember that oxidoreductases catalyse the transfer of hydrogen, oxygen or electrons between molecules, e.g. cytochrome oxidase is an enzyme that transfers electrons from cytochromes to oxygen (forming water) at the end of the electron transport chain in aerobic respiration.

(b) ATP supplies the energy needed for metabolic reactions ✓.

ℓ A correct answer for 1 mark. Overall, Candidate B scores 4 out of 5 marks for this question.

(3) (a) Nervous coordination uses specific cells (neurones) to transmit information, whereas hormones are transported in the blood ✓.

ℓ This is correct, but only *one* difference has been stated and so only 1 mark is awarded. If you are asked for *two* differences, you should give two (and only two). If a number of differences is *not* given, use the number of marks as a guide to how many points to make.

(b) There is a high concentration of sodium ions outside the cell ✓. Stimulation of the axon leads to an increase in the permeability of the cell surface membrane, causing an influx of sodium ions ✓ **(MAX)** which change the potential difference across the membrane from negative to positive.

 Candidate B receives full marks for this answer. Note that there are usually more points available on the marking scheme than the question is actually worth. You do not need to get *all* the points to get full marks — just two points in this case.

(c) The metabolic rate increases in order to generate ATP ✓ for the active transport of sodium ions out of the nerve cell to restore the resting potential ✓.

 This answer is correct for 2 marks. Remember that ATP is also needed for the release of neurotransmitter during the passage of an impulse across a synapse.

(d) It would reduce the concentration gradient between the inside and the outside of the axon ✓. Therefore, fewer sodium ions would enter the axon following stimulation, making an action potential less likely ✓.

 A very good answer for full marks. Overall, Candidate B scores 7 out of 8 marks for this question.

(4) (a) (i) The glucose concentration rises steadily from 7.6 nmol dm^{-3} at 30 minutes to 12 nmol dm^{-3} at 90 minutes ✓. It then falls back to its original level at 150 minutes ✓.

 An excellent answer, making good use of the figures from the graph.

(ii) The insulin concentration rises from 3 to 8.4 units. This represents a percentage increase of $[(8.4 - 3)/8.4] \times 100 = 64.3\%$ ✓✓.

 This answer is worth 2 out of 3 marks. The figures have been taken from the graph accurately and the difference (8.4 − 3) is used in the calculation. The method for the percentage calculation is incorrect — 3 units should have been used as the denominator (giving the correct answer of 180%), not 8.4 units. Remember that **percentage change = (change/original) × 100**. Note that you can have a percentage increase of more than 100%. Some students go back and change their response if they get more than 100%. Make sure that you avoid this error!

(iii) As the glucose concentration starts to rise, this stimulates the release of insulin from the β-cells in the islets of Langerhans in the pancreas ✓. As the glucose concentration continues to rise (due to absorption by the blood), more and more insulin is released ✓. Insulin eventually causes the concentration of glucose to fall by stimulating its uptake by liver and muscle cells ✓ **(MAX)**. This causes a decrease in insulin secretion (due to less glucose in the blood).

 An excellent answer, worth full marks.

(iv) Negative feedback is a mechanism used in homeostasis for maintaining optimum conditions in the body. If a physiological factor deviates from its optimum, the deviation is sensed and negative feedback mechanisms are used to return the factor to its optimum ✓. In this case, if the blood glucose level in the body rises, insulin is secreted from the pancreas which causes the glucose level to fall back to the optimum level ✓.

🖉 Full marks again for a very good answer.

(b) Glucagon can be used by the muscles for energy, but insulin is a hormone and cannot be used for energy ✗.

🖉 No marks for this answer. Candidate B may have confused glucagon (a hormone that causes blood glucose concentration to increase) with glycogen (a storage carbohydrate in animals). Glycogen *could* be broken down to glucose to provide energy for muscles, but it is never found in the blood. The correct answer is that **exercise causes rapid respiration in skeletal muscles. Therefore, homeostatic mechanisms will be required to stimulate the entry of glucose in the blood. Since glucagon causes a rise in blood glucose concentration, this hormone will be secreted by the pancreas (due to low blood glucose). Insulin (which causes the concentration of blood glucose to fall) will not be secreted, due to the low concentration of blood glucose.** Overall, Candidate B scores 9 out of 12 marks for this question.

(5) Anaerobic respiration is the breakdown of glucose in the absence of oxygen to yield energy ✓. It is essentially the same as glycolysis, which means that glucose is converted to pyruvate ✓ in the cytoplasm of the cell ✓. The biochemical reactions that take place during glycolysis are summarised by the equation:

$$\text{glucose} + 2\text{NAD (oxidised)} + 2\text{ADP} + 2\text{P}_i \checkmark$$

$$\downarrow$$

$$2 \times \text{pyruvate} + 2\text{NAD (reduced)} + 2\text{ATP} \checkmark\checkmark$$

Anaerobic respiration therefore yields only 2 molecules of ATP, which is only about 5–6% of that produced by aerobic respiration (which requires oxygen) ✓. In plants and microorganisms such as yeast, the pyruvate is then converted to ethanol and CO_2 ✓. In animals, the pyruvate is converted to lactic acid ✓. It is important that pyruvate is reduced to these products by NAD (reduced) in order to regenerate NAD (oxidised) ✓ **(MAX)**, so that glycolysis (and so ATP production) can continue.

🖉 This answer is worth 10 out of 10 marks. It is concise, accurate and detailed. Note that you can use equations (or diagrams) to summarise important information.

🖉 **Overall, Candidate B scores 34 out of 40 marks for this paper, which would be a grade A.**

ock paper

Answers to mock paper 2: Candidate A

(1) Hormones are usually either proteins, polypeptides, or ....lipids ✗.............. Most hormones are produced by ....exocrine ✗............. glands, which release them directly into the blood. Hormones bind to ....proteins ✓............ on the cell surface membrane of .....target ✓..... cells, where they bring about a response. The release of hormones is controlled by a mechanism known as....secretion ✗.

> ② Candidate A scores 2 out of 5 marks for this question. Hormones can be either proteins, polypeptides or **steroids/amines**. Although some biologists consider steroids to be a class of lipids, the answer 'lipids' in this context is too vague to earn a mark. Most hormones are produced by **endocrine** (ductless) glands, which secrete their products directly into the blood. It is quite common for students to confuse endocrine and exocrine glands, which secrete substances through a duct to their place of action. 'Proteins' is correct in the third space, although **receptors** would also have earned a mark. Finally, the release of hormones is controlled by a mechanism known as **negative feedback**.

(2) (a) A = dendrites ✓; B = axon ✓; C = myelin sheath ✓

> ② 3 out of 3 marks.

(b) The myelin sheath protects the neurone ✗.

> ② This answer suggests only *one* function and it is too vague to earn any marks. The myelin sheath **speeds up the conduction of nerve impulses** and **provides electrical insulation for the neurone**. Overall, Candidate A scores 3 out of 5 marks for this question.

(3) (a) Keeping things constant in the body ✓.

> ② This answer is very vague and only just worth 1 mark. Homeostasis is **the maintenance of a constant internal environment by using physiological mechanisms to regulate factors such as oxygen concentration, pH, temperature or water potential**.

(b) (i) Blood glucose concentrations are higher in curve A than in curve B throughout the experiment ✓. The blood glucose concentration returns to the starting value in curve B but remains higher than the starting value in curve A ✓.

> ② This answer is worth 2 out of 3 marks. Remember that you can include *similarities* in comparison questions, so Candidate A could have said that **both curves have a similar shape (an increase followed by a decrease)**. Alternatively,

Candidate A could have compared the *gradients* of the curves over a particular time period, for example, **curve B is steeper (a faster rate of change) than curve A between 0 and 60 minutes**.

(ii) Curve A, because it always has a higher glucose concentration than B ✓.

🖉 This is correct, but the explanation is too brief. Note that you will *not* get a mark for simply guessing curve A or B — an explanation is needed. Candidate A could have pointed out that **curve A does not return to its starting value over the 3 hour period**, or that **it shows a slow decrease in blood glucose concentration**. Overall, Candidate A scores 4 out of 8 marks for this question.

(4) (a) A = ethanol ✗; B = lactic acid ✗

🖉 Candidate A has mixed up these two products of anaerobic respiration. Remember that animals produce lactic acid and plants/microorganisms produce ethanol plus carbon dioxide. The CO_2 in the diagram should have acted as a clue!

(b) (i) They change colour to tell you how fast a reaction is going ✓.

🖉 This answer is too vague to earn more than 1 mark. **Redox indicators act as hydrogen acceptors and change colour when reduced** (methylene blue changes from blue to colourless). **The rate of colour change indicates the rate of reaction**. Redox indicators also demonstrate that dehydrogenase enzymes are involved.

(ii) Use the same concentration of sucrose ✓ to ensure that the results can be compared ✓.

🖉 Full marks for this part of the question. Candidate A could also have referred to controls regulating the quantity of yeast, the volume of indicator or the temperature.

(iii) $Q_{10} = 18.4 - 10.2 = 8.2$ arbitrary units ✗

🖉 Q_{10} is the increase in the rate of a process when the temperature is increased by 10°C. Q_{10} is known as the temperature coefficient and can be calculated from the simple formula given below:

$$Q_{10} = \frac{\text{rate of reaction at } (T + 10)°C}{\text{rate of reaction at } T°C}$$

In this case, $Q_{10} = 18.4/10.2 = 1.8$. Candidate A has used the correct figures but in an incorrect way!

(iv) Anaerobic respiration is enzyme-dependent ✓ and an increase in temperature will cause an increase in enzyme activity ✓.

🖉 Candidate A earns 2 out of 3 marks for this question. For the third mark, he or she could have explained *how* an increase in temperature causes an increase in enzyme activity, i.e. **the molecules have more kinetic energy and so more**

enzyme–substrate complexes are formed. Overall, Candidate A scores 5 out of 12 marks for this question.

(5) High blood pressure exists in the afferent arteriole of the renal artery due to its sudden narrowing to the glomerular capillaries ✓ and the smaller diameter of the efferent arteriole ✓. This pressure forces blood plasma (minus the large plasma proteins ✓) out of the glomerulus and through the basement membrane into Bowman's capsule ✓. This is known as ultrafiltration, or filtration on a molecular scale ✓, and results in glomerular filtrate which goes on to form urine.

　This answer is worth 5 out of 10 marks. It is a reasonably good account of ultra-filtration, but it makes no mention of selective reabsorption. To earn more marks, Candidate A should have described the changes in glomerular filtrate as it passes through the nephron, where selective reabsorption results in the formation of concentrated urine.

　Overall, Candidate A scores 19 out of 40 for this paper, which would be a grade D/E.

Answers to mock paper 2: Candidate B

(1) Hormones are usually either proteins, polypeptides, or ....steroids ✓.............. Most hormones are produced by ....endocrine ✓.............. glands, which release them directly into the blood. Hormones bind to ....receptors ✓............ on the cell surface membrane of .....liver ✗..... cells, where they bring about a response. The release of hormones is controlled by a mechanism known as....negative feedback ✓.

> 🖉 Candidate B scores 4 out of 5 marks for this question. Hormones *do* bind to receptors on the cell surface membrane of liver cells, but they also bind to many other types of cell. Therefore the answer 'liver' is too specific in the fourth space and **target cells** is a better alternative.

(2) (a) A = axons ✗; B = dendrite ✗; C = myelin sheath ✓

> 🖉 Candidate B scores 1 out of 3 marks for this part. He or she has mixed up the labels for axon (B) and dendrites (A). Remember that the axon is the elongated section of a neurone (nerve cell) which carries impulses away from the cell body while dendrites are the fine structures that form connections between the cell body of a neurone and the axons of other neurones.

(b) The myelin sheath speeds up the conduction of nerve impulses ✓ and provides electrical insulation for the neurone ✓.

> 🖉 A good, concise answer to part (b) gives Candidate B an overall score of 3 out of 5 marks for this question.

(3) (a) The maintenance of a constant internal environment ✓ by using physiological mechanisms to regulate important factors, such as body temperature (thermoregulation) ✓.

(b) (i) Blood glucose concentrations are higher in curve A than in curve B at every time-point throughout the experiment ✓. The blood glucose concentration returns to the starting value in curve B but remains higher than the starting value in curve A ✓. Both curves exhibit an increase and then a decrease in blood glucose concentration ✓.

(ii) Curve B, because diabetics do not have enough insulin to keep the blood glucose level high and so it is always lower than in curve A ✗.

> 🖉 No marks for part (ii). Candidate B has made the (fairly common) mistake of thinking that insulin causes the blood glucose concentration to *rise*. Insulin reduces blood glucose by stimulating the uptake of this monosaccharide by liver and muscle cells. Therefore, diabetics (who suffer from a lack of insulin) will often have a *higher* blood glucose concentration than non-diabetics, so curve A is the diabetic. Note that you will *not* get a mark for simply guessing curve A or B — an

explanation is needed. In addition to pointing out the overall concentration of glucose, Candidate B could have pointed out that **curve A does not return to its starting value observed over the 3 hour period**, or that **it shows a slow decrease in blood glucose concentration**. Overall, Candidate B scores 5 out of 8 marks for this question.

(4) (a) A = lactate ✓; B = ethanol ✓

(b) (i) Redox indicators act as hydrogen acceptors ✓. Methylene blue, for example, changes from blue to colourless when it is reduced by hydrogen ✓. The rate of colour change indicates the rate of reaction ✓ **(MAX)** so respiration reactions (which involve dehydrogenase enzymes) can be monitored.

A very good answer for 3 out of 3 marks.

(ii) Use the same temperature throughout ✓ to ensure that the results can be compared ✓.

Full marks. Candidate B could also have referred to controls regulating the quantity of yeast, the volume of indicator or the concentration of sucrose.

(iii) Q_{10} = 18.4/10.2 = 1.8 ✓✓

Correct. This was achieved using the temperature coefficient formula:

$$Q_{10} = \frac{\text{rate of reaction at } (T + 10)°C}{\text{rate of reaction at } T°C}$$

(iv) Anaerobic respiration is enzyme-dependent ✓, so an increase in temperature causes an increase in enzyme activity ✓. This is because the molecules in the system have more kinetic energy ✓ **(MAX)** and so more enzyme–substrate complexes are formed, leading to more product (per unit time).

An excellent final answer means that Candidate B scores the maximum 12 out of 12 marks for this question.

(5) Ultrafiltration is filtration on a molecular scale ✓. High blood pressure in the capillaries of the glomerulus ✓ forces fluid through the basement membrane into the Bowman's capsule of a kidney nephron ✓. This fluid is known as glomerular filtrate and has the same composition as blood plasma, except that it does not contain plasma proteins (which are too large to pass through the basement membrane of the capillaries) ✓. Useful substances, such as glucose, amino acids and some salts and water ✓, are then reabsorbed back into the blood as the filtrate passes through the nephron. Most reabsorption takes place in the proximal convoluted tubule ✓. The cells lining this tubule are adapted for this purpose in two ways:
- they have a brush border of microvilli ✓ providing a large surface area over which diffusion, facilitated diffusion and active transport can take place ✓
- they possess large numbers of mitochondria ✓ to provide the ATP necessary for the active transport of molecules such as glucose ✓ **(MAX)**

Further reabsorption and concentration take place in the loop of Henle, distal convoluted tubule and collecting duct. The end product is a relatively concentrated solution of urea (the main nitrogenous waste product of mammals), salts and water, known as urine, which passes out of the body via the bladder.

🖉 A very good free-prose answer — concise, detailed and relevant. This scores the maximum mark of 10 out of 10.

🖉 **Overall, Candidate B scores 34 out of 40 for this paper, which would be a grade A.**

Answers to mock paper 3: Candidate A

(1)

Statement	Rod cells		Cone cells	
Contain the pigment rhodopsin	✗	✗	✔	✗
Used for colour vision	✗	✗	✔	✔
Sensitive to light	✗	✗	✔	✔
Found mainly in the fovea	✗	✔	✔	✔
Work most efficiently at low light intensities	✔	✔	✗	✔

Six responses out of 10 correct, which is worth 3 out of 5 marks. Candidate A seems to have mixed up the pigments rhodopsin and iodopsin in the first line. Remember that **rhodopsin is found in rod cells and iodopsin is found in cone cells**. The response in the 'rod cells' box on the second line *might* be a cross (which would be correct), but it also looks a little like a tick. Because it is ambiguous, no mark is awarded. The final mistake is in the 'rod cells' box on the third line. Both rods and cones are sensitive to light as they are both photoreceptors!

(2) (a) W = water ✗; X = oxygen ✓

Candidate A scores 1 out of 2 marks. Molecule W is carbon dioxide, which is released during the link reaction and the Krebs cycle.

(b) Y = hydrolysis ✗; Z = oxidative phosphorylation ✓

1 mark again. Process Y is **glycolysis**. For Z, the answer **electron transport chain** would also be correct.

(c) In mitochondria ✗

This answer is not wrong, but it is not specific enough to earn a mark. The correct answer is **in the matrix of a mitochondrion**. Overall, Candidate A scores 2 out of 5 marks for this question.

(3) (a) (i) −70 ✗

Although Candidate A has found the correct value for the resting potential, he or she has forgotten the units (mV) and therefore does not earn the mark.

(ii) Sodium gates open so the membrane becomes permeable to sodium ions ✓. Therefore, sodium ions move out of the axon ✗.

🖉 This answer is worth 1 out of 2 marks. There is an excess of sodium ions *outside* the axon when the neurone is at rest, therefore depolarisation (between X and Y) is caused by **sodium ions entering the axon.**

(b) (i) Vesicles ✓; sodium ✓

(ii) It stops the nerves working and so the person dies ✗.

🖉 The answer to part (ii) is far too vague (and too brief) to earn any marks. **Curare in the bloodstream will be absorbed by nervous tissue. Therefore, the curare molecules will compete with acetylcholine, reducing the quantity of the neuro-transmitter that is bound to the post-synaptic membrane. This may cause paralysis which, if it affects the muscles involved in ventilation, may lead to death by respiratory failure.** Overall, Candidate A scores 3 out of 8 marks for this question.

(4) (a) (i) In the brain ✗

🖉 This answer is correct, but not specific enough to earn the mark. Osmoreceptors are found in the **hypothalamus** (within the brain).

(ii) The pituitary gland ✓

🖉 This is fine for 1 mark. To be even more specific, ADH is produced by the **posterior lobe of the pituitary gland.**

(b) It will fall ✓.

🖉 This is correct, but certainly not worth 3 marks! Candidate A should have explained *why* the water potential falls. If less ADH is released, less water will be reabsorbed back into the blood from the kidneys. Therefore, large quantities of watery urine will be produced. The blood will have less water in it and therefore have a lower (more negative) water potential.

(c) $17.5 = 0.72x + 4$ ✓; so $0.72x = 17.5 - 4 = 13.5$ ✓

Therefore, $x = 13.5/0.72 = 18.75$ mm ✓

🖉 An excellent answer (with units), with working set out clearly, for full marks.

(d) Long loops of Henle and high concentrations of ADH will mean that a lot of water is reabsorbed back into the blood from the kidney nephrons ✓. This is needed because there is not much water for the animals to drink ✓.

🖉 This answer is worth 2 out of 4 marks. Candidate A could have explained *how* longer loops of Henle and high concentrations of ADH result in greater water reabsorption. **Movement of ions across the walls of the loop of Henle enables it to act as a countercurrent multiplier, building up the concentration of sodium in the medulla of the kidney. This process results in the reabsorption of water by osmosis and the production of concentrated urine in the collecting duct. ADH causes the walls of the collecting ducts to become more permeable to water, so more water is reabsorbed and concentrated urine is produced.**

These adaptive factors therefore lead to greater water retention in arid environments. Overall, Candidate A scores 7 out of 12 marks for this question.

(5) The concentration of glucose in the blood is controlled by insulin ✓. This hormone is secreted in response to an increased blood glucose concentration ✓ and brings about a reduction in glucose by two mechanisms. There is an increased rate of glucose uptake by cells ✓ and enzymes are activated that convert glucose to glycogen ✓. Therefore, glucose is kept at a relatively stable concentration.

This answer is worth 4 out of 10 marks. It is a reasonable (if brief) account of the role of *insulin* in *lowering* blood glucose, but does not mention the role of *glucagon* (or adrenaline) in *raising* blood glucose. For a more detailed account, see Candidate B's response to this question.

Overall, Candidate A scores 19 out of 40 for this paper, which would be a grade D/E.

Answers to mock paper 3: Candidate B

(1)

Statement	Rod cells	Cone cells
Contain the pigment rhodopsin	✔ ✓	✗ ✓
Used for colour vision	✗ ✓	✔ ✓
Sensitive to light	✔ ✓	✔ ✓
Found mainly in the fovea	✔ ✗	✗ ✗
Work most efficiently at low light intensities	✗ ✗	✔ ✗

Candidate B got 6 responses out of 10 correct, which is worth 3 out of 5 marks. He or she seems to have mixed up the location of the different photoreceptors in the fourth line. Remember that **cones are found mainly in the fovea** and that **rods are found throughout the retina** (but not in the fovea). Candidate B has also mixed up rods and cones in terms of their sensitivity to light (bottom line). Rods are very sensitive to light and are actually bleached at high light intensities, and this is why rods are used for night vision. Cones require relatively high light intensities to function efficiently.

(2) (a) W = CO_2 ✓; X = oxygen ✓
   (b) Y = glycolysis ✓; Z = electron transport chain ✓

Correct, for 2 marks each. Note that the answer **oxidative phosphorylation** for process Z is also correct.

(c) In the matrix of a mitochondrion ✓

Accurate answers throughout. Overall, Candidate B scores 5 out of 5 marks for this question.

(3) (a) (i) −70 mV ✓

1 mark. Remember to give the units.

   (ii) Sodium gates open, making the membrane permeable to sodium ions ✓. Therefore, sodium ions move into the axon, causing the change in membrane potential between X and Y ✓.
   (b) (i) Vesicles ✓; sodium ✓.
   (ii) Curare will be absorbed by nervous tissue in the body ✓. The curare molecules will bind to receptors on the post-synaptic membrane, preventing

acetylcholine from binding ✓ and therefore inhibiting the transmission of nerve impulses between neurones ✓ **(MAX)**. This may cause paralysis in the muscles that are involved in ventilation and so cause death by respiratory failure.

📝 A very good answer, giving Candidate B full marks for this question.

(4) (a) (i) In the hypothalamus ✓
(ii) The adrenal gland ✗

📝 Part (ii) is incorrect. Students often confuse ADH with adrenaline, which *is* secreted by the adrenal gland. The correct answer is the **pituitary gland**.

(b) Inhibition of ADH release will cause less water to be reabsorbed from the nephrons back into the blood ✓. Therefore, more urine will be produced and the water content of the blood will fall ✓, i.e. it will have a lower (more negative) water potential ✓.

📝 This is correct, for 3 marks.

(c) $y = (0.72 \times 17.5) + 4 = 16.6$ ✗

📝 This is incorrect and earns no marks. Candidate B has mixed up x and y and entered the figure for concentration (17.5 arbitrary units) as the figure for length. Furthermore, there are no units included in the answer. In this case, the question asks the candidate to find x (given the value of y) and so the equation has to be rearranged, i.e. $x = (y - 4)/0.72 = 18.75$ mm.

(d) Movement of ions across the walls of the loop of Henle enables it to act as a countercurrent multiplier, building up the concentration of sodium in the medulla of the kidney ✓. This process results in the reabsorption of water by osmosis and the production of concentrated urine in the collecting duct ✓. High concentrations of ADH will mean that the collecting ducts are more permeable to water ✓ and so a lot of water is reabsorbed back into the blood from the kidney nephrons ✓ **(MAX)**. These adaptive mechanisms help the animals to conserve water in dry environments.

📝 This is a very good answer, worth 4 out of 4 marks. Overall, Candidate B scores 8 out of 12 marks for this question.

(5) The blood glucose level is the concentration of glucose circulating in the blood plasma. The concentration of glucose in the blood is typically 3.4–5.6 millimoles per dm^3. It is important to maintain this concentration between certain limits and the hormones insulin and glucagon play an important role in this process ✓. If the glucose concentration falls too low (hypoglycaemia), the central nervous system ceases to function correctly. If it rises too high (hyperglycaemia), there will be a loss of glucose from the blood in the urine ✓.

The regulation of glucose concentration in the blood is a good example of homeostasis. Insulin is secreted by β-cells in the islets of Langerhans ✓ in the pancreas in response to an increased blood glucose concentration ✓ and brings about a reduction in glucose by two mechanisms. There is an increased rate of glucose uptake by cells (particularly liver and muscle cells) ✓ and enzymes are activated that convert glucose to glycogen ✓. The process by which an increase in the concentration of glucose initiates mechanisms to decrease the glucose concentration is called negative feedback ✓. Glucagon is secreted by α-cells in the islets of Langerhans ✓ in response to a decreased blood glucose concentration ✓ and brings about an increase in glucose by two mechanisms. Gluconeogenesis is stimulated ✓ **(MAX)** and enzymes are activated that convert glycogen to glucose.

☑ An excellent answer for 10 out of 10 marks.

☑ **Overall, Candidate B scores 34 out of 40 marks for this paper, which would be a grade A.**